EULENBURG AUDIO+SCORE

Edvard Grieg

Holberg Suite
Op. 40

Sigurd Jorsalfar
Op. 56

Edited by / Herausgegeben von
Richard Clarke / John Horton

EULENBURG

EAS 183
ISBN 978-3-7957-6583-5
ISMN 979-0-2002-2602-7

© 2013 Ernst Eulenburg & Co GmbH, Mainz
for Europe excluding the British Isles
Ernst Eulenburg Ltd, London
for all other countries
Edition based on Eulenburg Study Score ETP 897 & 1372
CD ℗ 2011 & 2007 Naxos Rights International Ltd
CD © 2013 Ernst Eulenburg Ltd, London

Ernst Eulenburg Ltd
48 Great Marlborough Street
London W1F 7BB

Contents / Inhalt

Preface   VII

Vorwort   XII

Holberg Suite

I.   Praeludium. Allegro vivace   1   Track 1

II.   Sarabande. Andante   6   Track 2

Allegretto

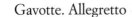

Musette. Poco più mosso

Poco più mosso

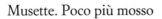

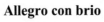

IV.   Air. Andante religioso   12   Track ④

Andante religioso

V.   Rigaudon. Allegro con brio   16   Track ⑤

Allegro con brio

Sigurd Jorsalfar

I.   Prelude (In the King's Hall).
         Allegretto semplice   21   Track ⑥

Allegretto semplice

II.   Intermezzo (Borghild's Dream). Poco andante   28   Track ⑦

Poco Andante

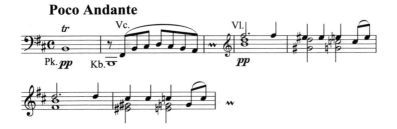

III.   Homage March. Allegro molto   38   Track ⑧

Allegro molto

Preface

Holberg Suite
Composed: 1884 in Lofthus
First performance: 13 March 1885 in Bergen, conducted by the composer
Original publisher: Peters, Leipzig, 1884
Instrumentation: String orchestra
Duration: ca. 20 minutes

'Powdered-wig music'! Thus, Grieg described – probably not without a wink – his *Holberg Suite*, thereby simultaneously comprehending the historical character of this unique work that claimed an exceptional position in the composer's complete works. If his previous compositions were distinguished above all by the close connection with his Nordic native country, be it through folk elements or through the capturing of nature impressions, then with the *Holberg Suite* he pursued a completely new path. The indications for the movements alone, *Präludium, Sarabande, Gavotte, Air* and *Rigaudon*, refer to the model of the French suite, just as the additional remark, 'in the old style', underscores the reversion to baroque forms. On 26 August 1884, Grieg reported for the first time on 'my old-fashioned suite *Aus Holbergs Zeit*, which I have finished'.[1] Moreover, he did not refrain from referring to the exceptional character of his newest work: 'As an exception, it is actually a good exercise for concealing one's own personality'.[2]

The commission for the composition had reached Grieg a few weeks before, in Lofthus where he was spending the summer of 1884 with his wife. The immediate reason for the instrumental piece, not more closely defined, were the honours organized by the city of Bergen for the 200th birthday of the Danish-Norwegian poet Ludvig Holberg. Grieg's interest was immediately aroused, and the commission brought to an end, at least for the short-term, the break in creativity that – aside from several small arrangements of his own pieces – had already lasted since autumn, a break that may possibly in the end be put down to the composer's eventful circumstances. After a separation, at first apparently final, Nina and Edvard Grieg were reconciled again in January and now, after a longer concert tour, were in the middle of blueprints for Troldhaugen ('Trollhügel'), their new estate. Full of enthusiasm, Grieg devoted himself to this entirely new challenge, as is shown by his words to the composer Nils Ravnkilde: 'No opus up to now has made me feel more enthusiastic than this.'

---

[1] Quoted from Norbert Brendt: 'Griegs Suite *Aus Holbergs Zeit* op. 40', in: *Kongreßbericht – 1. Deutscher Edvard-Grieg-Kongreß* (Altenmedingen, 1996), 51
[2] Ibid., 51

Grieg now gave himself with the same energy to the unexpected composing commission on a subject of special interest to himself. For some time already, Holberg had represented a figure with whom the composer identified. And thus, that he was inspired by the poet's times is hardly to be wondered at. Just as the baroque dance movements unmistakably formed the foundation of the suite initially conceived as a piano work, so Grieg's own tonal language, interwoven with the historical model, is not to be ignored.

The *Präludium* already plays with the mixture of various styles. The terse, urgent rhythm dominating the entire movement clearly refers to the archetype of the same name. Yet the formal conception of the first movement already distances itself from these roots. On closer examination, this proves to be a miniature sonata movement. Out of the clear-cut pulse of the music, the first theme soars upwards like a fanfare, followed, only a few bars later in the first violin, by the second, clearly cantabile theme with its characteristic falling fifth, whose melody is carried downwards in contrast to the first theme. In the development-like section inserted into it, there are now at first the echoes of the first theme, which are framed by falling, broken seventh chords in the cello and filled out in the violas. After the sweeping melodic flourishes that generously exploit the tonal space, the driving, omnipresent pulse, now in the second violin, adheres to the pitch b, whereas the first violins, with their lyrical counter accent in their characteristic style, recall the second theme. The first theme moves into ever more space until finally at the conclusion it dominates – at the last, in its inversion – the whole musical event. Only at the last hearing of the second theme does the driving force momentarily recede into the background.

The succession of the actual dance movements is now opened by the short *Sarabande*, one of the key movements of the baroque suite. In particular, it clearly reveals as such the characteristic emphasis on the second beat. Small, melodic intervals mainly of seconds as well as pitch repetitions which not infrequently have the effect of an adherence to this pitch, create, on the one hand, calming influences and reinforce, on the other, its character as a measured dance. The middle section clearly gets its material from the opening eight bars. Thus, the first violins play with the melodic building blocks from bar 2, each time in a modified form. A murky echo immediately reverberates in the violas, until finally the cellos take over the direction with another melody fragment. The entrance of the strings in octaves interrupts their melancholy playing and introduces anew the complete repetition of the whole thematic complex, at the same time closing the *Sarabande*.

With the *Gavotte* the music again takes on a happy mood. The whole is characterized within a tripartite form. The first statement of the *Gavotte* is followed by the embedded *Musette*. A repetition of the *Gavotte* once again concludes this movement. This same orgnization is found even in the *Musette*. A contrasting middle section is framed by two similar formal sections. Formally, the *Gavotte* can be understood as a rondo. The first section is based on an eight-bar period in which both halves are nearly identical. The central theme consists of a melody line initially rising upwards to the sixth with sharp accentuation on every first and third beat, before it returns again in a larger curve to the point of departure. The period is heard altogether three times. Two added, contrasting sections form with them the caesura.

Even in the much-praised *Air* two similarly constructed corner sections surround the middle section. The movement clearly refers to the already introduced thematic material, and yet it is completely distinct in its tone colour. In melancholy minor, the central melodic idea makes a stately appearance which is immediately repeated a whole tone lower. The theme of the middle section is derived from it, yet appears in an entirely other form. Radiant D major brightens the music. The musical idea of the sixteenth-group is split off from it and develops in mounting dynamics. With cutting dissonant seconds the theme is heard again finally in minor, this time carried by the low tones of the cello.

The *Rigaudon* concludes the suite in a cheerful tone of voice. The pounding tempo of the first part stands in abrupt contrast to the rather stately middle section. Broken chords as well as extended chains of eighths, also consisting of large leaps, form the beginning of the *Rigaudon*, however, scale motions predominate in the middle part before the repetition of the first section brings a resurgence of the clear baroque joie de vivre.

Despite all rhythmic, formal and also figurative analogies with the French suite, the *Holberg Suite* cannot deny its romantic features. Especially in the form enriched with chromatic and dissonant elements, Grieg's own musical language shimmers through again and again and at the same time makes up its entirely special charm. Even though the version of the *Holberg Suite* presented here already enjoyed a special popularity in the lifetime of the composer, we should not forget that it first originated out of the reworking of the piano version in which it was first heard at the Holberg festival. The string version was finally premiered in March 1885 and has, up to the present time, been chosen for concert programmes in this form.

Sandra Borzikowski
Translation: Margit McCorkle

Sigurd Jorsalfar
Composed: 1870 in Christiania
First performance: 17 May 1870 in Christiania
Original publisher: Peters, Leipzig
Instrumentation:
Prelude (In the King's Hall): 2 Flutes, 2 Oboes, 2 Clarinets, 2 Bassoons –
4 Horns, 2 Trumpets, 3 Trombones – Timpani – Strings
Intermezzo (Borghild's Dream): 2 Flutes, 2 Oboes, 2 Clarinets, 2 Bassoons –
4 Horns – Timpani, Cymbals, Triangle – Strings
Homage March: 2 Flutes, 2 Oboes, 2 Clarinets, 2 Bassoons – 4 Horns,
3 Trumpets, 3 Trombones, Tuba – Timpani, Snare Drum, Bass Drum,
Triangle, Cymbals, Harp – Strings
Duration: ca. 17 minutes

The Norwegian writer Bjørnstjerne Bjørnson (1832–1910), like his slightly older contemporary Henrik Ibsen, began his career as a dramatist with plays based on Norse saga literature. Bjørnson's *Sigurd Jorsalfar* ('the Crusader') was written in 1872. It deals with the rivalries and eventual reconciliation of the brother kings, Øjstejn and Sigurd, who reigned jointly over Norway in the heroic age of the twelfth century. Øjstejn (or Eystein) remained in Norway, ruling with justice and wisdom, and building roads, harbours, and churches, while Sigurd went on crusades, fought valiantly, and admired the wonders of Byzantium and the Holy Land. Bjørnson clearly regarded the two men as symbols of diametrically opposite tendencies in the national character, and thus stressed in dramatic form the need for nineteenth century Norwegians to balance their impulse towards exploration, missionary activities, and overseas settlement against the development and consolidation of social, economic, and political institutions within the homeland itself.

Grieg was invited to compose incidental music for the first production of Bjørnson's play in Christiania on Constitution Day, 17 May 1872. The three orchestral pieces and two vocal numbers he provided were published soon afterwards in piano score by Lose of Copenhagen as the composer's Op.22. In 1892 the instrumental movements were revised for full orchestra and republished by Peters of Leipzig as Grieg's Op.56. At the opening of the new Norwegian National Theatre in 1898 there was a revival of the play with the original music further revised by the composer, and there was yet another important production in 1905 in honour of the accession of Haakon VII to the throne of a completely independent Norway. In the meantime the orchestral suite had established itself internationally on the concert platform, though it never quite equalled the music of *Peer Gynt* in popularity.

The following are the three movements of Grieg's Op.56:

1. Prelude: 'In the King's Hall'. Originally entitled 'At the Matching Game', this march was intended as an introduction to Act II of the drama. 'The Matching Game' refers to the scene

in which the brothers enumerate and compare their personal merits as men and rulers. Formal emulation of this kind was a traditional Viking pastime, meant to entertain the company sitting at their ale, but as the scene continues rivalry becomes more bitter, arousing particular hostility in the moody King Sigurd, and gradually involving the personal followers of both the protagonists. Grieg's music is based on a Gavotte for violin and piano dating from 1867.

2. Intermezzo: 'Borghild's Dream'. Described as 'Introduction and Melodrama', this music provides a setting for the scene in Act I where Borghild, daughter of Olaf of Dal, awakes from troubled dreams in her father's house. Her close friendship with King Øjstejn has given rise to gossip, and to prove her innocence she has submitted to the ordeal of walking over red-hot iron. Soon afterwards, ill-feeling between the Kings is intensified when Sigurd, who also is under the spell of her beauty, attempts to abduct her from her home. The music closely follows Bjørnson's elaborate stage directions:

'Quiet music begins before the curtain goes up, and as it rises depicts her restless sleep with weary, subdued passages, until it mounts into acute dread. She cries out, awakes, and starts up. The music depicts the confused waking thoughts that crowd upon her, until it ceases while she whispers, 'I am still walking over the red-hot iron'. The music again follows her as she slowly advances, stops, and leans against the back of a chair... [Here a lengthy monologue in verse follows] ... The music subsides in quiet grief, until it ends with a sudden jerk, and she rises to her feet.'

To produce the required atmosphere, Grieg uses such orchestral devices as muffled timpani rolls, stopped horn notes, two-finger pizzicati, piccolos momentarily, replacing the two flutes, strokes on triangle and cymbals, and violent dynamic contrasts.

3. 'Homage March' (Hyldningsmarsjen). This occurs in Act III, introducing the scene in which the Kings are reconciled. A stage direction indicates that as the brothers make their peace with each other, and go out hand in hand, the music is to begin with a grave introduction, and then change to the 'Homage March' itself. The scene is now set for the council or *husthing*, at which the Kings announce their final reconciliation. This movement underwent considerable revision and expansion, among the later additions being the fanfares for brass (commencing b165), and the Trio (commencing b76) with harp chords, which is reminiscent of the Minuet-Trio of the Piano Sonata, Op.7, written in 1865. It is also interesting to note the similarity between the main theme of the 'Homage March', assigned first to four-part solo cellos, and the slow movement of the Cello Sonata, Op.36 (1882–3).

John Horton

Vorwort

Aus Holbergs Zeit
komponiert: 1884 in Lofthus
Uraufführung: 13. März 1885 in Bergen, unter Leitung des Komponisten
Originalverlag: Peters, Leipzig, 1884
Orchesterbesetzung: Streichorchester
Spieldauer: etwa 20 Minuten

„Perückenstück"! So bezeichnete Grieg – wohl nicht ohne ein Augenzwinkern – seine *Holberg-Suite* und erfasste damit gleichzeitig den historisierenden Charakter seines einzigartigen Werkes, das eine Ausnahmestellung im Gesamtwerk des Komponisten beansprucht. Zeichneten sich seine bisherigen Kompositionen vor allem durch die enge Verknüpfung mit seiner nordischen Heimat aus, sei es durch volkstümliche Elemente oder durch das Einfangen von Naturimpressionen, so beschritt er mit der Komposition *Aus Holbergs Zeit* einen vollkommen neuen Weg. Alleine die Satzbezeichnungen *Präludium, Sarabande, Gavotte, Air* und *Rigaudon* verweisen auf das Vorbild der französischen Suite, ebenso wie der Zusatz „im alten Style" den Rückgriff auf barocke Formen unterstreicht. Am 26. August 1884 berichtet Grieg zum ersten Mal über „meine altmodische Suite *Aus Holbergs Zeit*, die ich fertig gemacht habe."[1] Zudem versäumt Grieg nicht, auf das exzeptionelle Gepräge seines neuesten Werkes hinzuweisen: „Es ist eigentlich als Ausnahme eine gute Übung, seine eigene Persönlichkeit zu verstecken."[2]

Der Kompositionsauftrag hatte Grieg einige Wochen zuvor in Lofthus erreicht, wo er gemeinsam mit seiner Frau den Sommer 1884 verlebte. Anlass für das nicht näher definierte Instrumentalstück waren die Ehrungen zum 200. Geburtstag des dänisch-norwegischen Dichters Ludvig Holberg, veranstaltet von der Stadt Bergen. Griegs Interesse war sofort geweckt, und der Auftrag beendete – von einigen kleinen Bearbeitungen eigener Stücke einmal abgesehen – zumindest kurzzeitig die bereits seit Herbst andauernde Schaffenspause, die möglicherweise nicht zuletzt auf die ereignisreichen Lebensumstände des Komponisten zurückzuführen ist. Nach einer zunächst endgültig erscheinenden Trennung hatten Nina und Edvard Grieg im Januar wieder zueinander gefunden und steckten nun, nach einer längeren Konzertreise, mitten in den Entwürfen zu Troldhaugen („Trollhügel"), ihrem neuen Anwesen. Dieser gänzlich neuen Herausforderung widmete sich Grieg voller Enthusiasmus,

---

[1] Zitiert nach Norbert Brendt: „Griegs Suite *Aus Holbergs Zeit* op. 40", in: *Kongreßbericht – 1. Deutscher Edvard-Grieg-Kongreß*, Altenmedingen 1996, S. 51.
[2] Ebd., S. 51.

wovon seine an den Komponisten Nils Ravnkilde gerichteten Worte zeugen: „Kein Opus hat mich bisher mehr begeistert als dieses." Mit gleicher Energie begab sich Grieg nun an den unverhofften Kompositionsauftrag, der ihm ein besonderes Anliegen war. Holberg stellte bereits seit geraumer Zeit eine Identifikationsfigur für den Komponisten dar. Und so ist es auch kaum verwunderlich, dass er sich von der Zeit des Dichters inspirieren ließ. So unverkennbar die barocken Tanzsätze die Grundlage für die zunächst als Klavierwerk konzipierte Suite bildeten, so unüberhörbar ist Griegs eigene Tonsprache mit der historischen Vorlage verwoben.

Bereits das *Präludium* spielt mit der Vermischung unterschiedlicher Stile. Die prägnante, drängende Rhythmik, die den ganzen Satz beherrscht, verweist deutlich auf den gleichnamigen Archetyp. Doch schon die formale Anlage des ersten Satzes entfernt sich von diesen Wurzeln. Bei genauerer Betrachtung erweist sich dieser als eine Kleinform des Sonatensatzes. Aus dem markanten Puls der Musik schwingt sich fanfarenartig das erste Thema empor, dem nur wenige Takte später in den ersten Geigen das zweite, deutlich kantablere Thema mit seinem charakteristischen Quintfall, dessen Melodie im Gegensatz zum ersten Thema abwärts geführt wird, folgt. Im darauf einsetzenden durchführungsartigen Teil sind es nun zunächst die Anklänge an das erste Thema, die sich eingerahmt von fallenden, gebrochenen Septakkorden im Cello und umspielt auch in den Bratschen herauskristallisieren. Nach den ausladenden Melodiefloskeln, die den Tonraum großzügig ausnutzen, verharrt der vorantreibende, omnipräsente Puls nun in den zweiten Geigen auf dem Ton h, während die ersten Violinen mit ihrem lyrischen Gegenakzent in ihrem Duktus an das zweite Thema erinnern. Das erste Thema erobert sich jedoch immer mehr Raum, bis es zum Abschluss endgültig – zuletzt in seiner Umkehrung – das gesamte musikalische Geschehen dominiert. Lediglich das letztmalige Erklingen des zweiten Themas drängt für einen kurzen Moment die treibende Kraft in den Hintergrund.

Die Folge der eigentlichen Tanzsätze wird nun durch die kurze *Sarabande*, einem der Kernsätze der barocken Suite, eröffnet. Insbesondere die charakteristische Betonung der zweiten Zählzeit weist sie offenkundig als solche aus. Kleine, überwiegend aus Sekunden bestehende Melodieschritte sowie Tonwiederholungen, die nicht selten ein Verharren auf diesem Ton zur Folge haben, schaffen einerseits Ruhepole und bekräftigen andererseits ihren Charakter als Schreittanz. Der Mittelteil bezieht sein musikalisches Material klar aus den eröffnenden acht Takten. So spielen die ersten Violinen mit dem Melodiebaustein aus Takt 2, jeweils in modifizierter Form. Ein düsteres Echo hallt dabei sogleich in den Bratschen nach, bis schließlich die Celli mit einem weiteren Melodiefragment die Führung übernehmen. Der Einsatz der oktaviert geführten Streicher unterbricht deren melancholisches Spiel und leitet eine erneute, vollständige Wiederholung des gesamten Themenkomplexes ein, die zugleich die *Sarabande* beschließt.

Mit der *Gavotte* nimmt die Musik wieder eine ausgelassene Stimmung an. Eine Dreiteiligkeit bestimmt hier die Großform, setzt sich aber auch in der kleineren Einheit fort. Dem ersten Durchlauf der *Gavotte* folgt die eingebettete *Musette*. Eine abermalige Wiederholung der Gavotte beendet diesen Satz. Auch in der *Musette* findet sich diese Anlage. Ein kontrastierender Mittelteil wird von zwei gleichen Formteilen umrahmt. Die *Gavotte* kann ihrer Form nach als Rondo verstanden werden. Der erste Teil beruht auf einer achttaktigen Periode, wobei deren beide Hälften annähernd identisch sind. Das zentrale Thema besteht aus einer zunächst nach oben, zur Sexte strebenden Melodielinie mit scharfen Akzentuierungen der jeweils ersten und dritten Zählzeit, bevor sie in einem größeren Bogen wieder zur Ausgangs-position zurückkehrt. Insgesamt erklingt diese Periode dreimal. Zwei eingefügte, kontrastie-rende Formteile bilden dabei die Zäsur.

Auch in der viel gerühmten *Air* schließen zwei gleichartig gestaltete Eckteile den Mittelteil ein. Der Satz nimmt deutlich Bezug auf das bereits vorgestellte thematische Material, und doch unterscheidet er sich vollkommen in seinem Kolorit. Getragen, in schwermütigem Moll tritt der zentrale melodische Einfall in Erscheinung, der sogleich ein Ganzton tiefer wieder-holt wird. Aus ihm leitet sich das Thema des Mittelteils ab, doch erscheint es in gänzlich anderer Gestalt. Strahlendes Dur hellt die Musik auf. Der musikalische Gedanke der Sech-zehntelgruppe wird daraus abgespalten und in steigender Dynamik entwickelt. Mit schnei-denden Sekundreibungen erklingt das Thema letztlich wieder in Moll, diesmal getragen von den tiefen Klängen des Cello.

Der *Rigaudon* beschließt in heiterem Tonfall die Suite. Das peitschende Tempo des ersten Teils steht im schroffen Gegensatz zum eher getragenen Mittelteil. Gebrochene Akkorde sowie ausgedehnte, auch aus großen Sprüngen bestehende Achtelketten formieren den Beginn des *Rigaudon*, Skalenbewegungen überwiegen hingegen im Mittelteil, bevor die Wiederholung des ersten Abschnitts die ungetrübte barocke Lebensfreude wiederaufleben lässt.

Trotz aller rhythmischen, formalen und auch figurativen Analogien mit der französischen Suite kann die *Holberg-Suite* ihre romantischen Züge nicht negieren. Insbesondere die mit chromatischen und dissonanten Elementen angereicherte harmonische Gestaltung lässt immer wieder Griegs eigene musikalische Sprache durchschimmern und macht zugleich deren ganz besonderen Reiz aus. Auch wenn sich die hier vorgestellte Fassung der *Holberg-Suite* bereits zu Lebzeiten des Komponisten besonderer Popularität erfreute, darf nicht über-sehen werden, dass sie erst aus der Überarbeitung der Klavierfassung, die zuerst beim Hol-berg-Fest erklang, entstanden ist. Die Streicherfassung kam schließlich im März des Jahres 1885 zur Uraufführung und bestimmt in dieser Gestalt bis heute die Konzertprogramme.

Sandra Borzikowski

Sigurd Jorsalfar
komponiert: 1870 in Christiania
Uraufführung: 17. Mai 1870 in Christiania
Originalverlag: Peters, Leipzig
Orchesterbesetzung:
Vorspiel (In der Königshalle): 2 Flöten, 2 Oboen, 2 Klarinetten, 2 Fagotte –
4 Hörner, 2 Trompeten, 3 Posaunen – Pauken – Streicher
Intermezzo (Borghilds Traum): 2 Flöten, 2 Oboen, 2 Klarinetten,
2 Fagotte – 4 Hörner – Pauken, Becken, Triangel – Streicher
Huldigungsmarsch: 2 Flöten, 2 Oboen, 2 Klarinetten, 2 Fagotte – 4 Hörner,
3 Trompeten, 3 Posaunen, Tuba – Pauken, kleine Trommel, große Trommel,
Triangel, Becken, Harfe – Streicher
Spieldauer: etwa 17 Minuten

Wie sein etwas älterer Zeitgenosse Henrik Ibsen, begann der norwegische Schriftsteller Bjørnstjerne Bjørnson (1832–1910) seine Karriere als Schauspieldichter mit Stücken, deren Stoff aus der Literatur der norwegischen Sagen stammte. Bjørnson schrieb *Sigurd Jorsalfar* („Der Kreuzfahrer") im Jahre 1872. Das Stück handelt von dem Wettstreit und der späteren Versöhnung zweier Könige, Øjstejn und Sigurd, die Brüder waren und im Heldenzeitalter des 12. Jh. gemeinsam Norwegen regierten. Øjstejn (oder Eystein) blieb in Norwegen und regierte gerecht und weise, baute Straßen, Häfen und Kirchen, während Sigurd auf Kreuzzüge ging, tapfer stritt und sich von den Wundern in Byzanz und im Heiligen Land beeindrucken ließ. Offenbar hat Bjørnson die beiden Männer als Symbole für die gegensätzlichen Neigungen ihres Nationalcharakters angesehen und daher in dramatischer Form die Notwendigkeit für die Norweger des neunzehnten Jahrhunderts betont, ihren impulsiven Hang zu Entdeckungsfahrten, Missionen und Überseesiedlungen mit der Entwicklung und Festigung der sozialen, wirtschaftlichen und politischen Institutionen im eigenen Lande ins Gleichgewicht zu bringen.

Grieg wurde ersucht, die Bühnenmusik für die Erstaufführung von Bjørnsons Stück am Verfassungstag, 17. Mai 1872 in Christiania, zu schreiben. Die drei Orchesterstücke und zwei Gesangsnummern, die er dafür komponierte, wurden bald darauf im Klavierauszug von Lose in Kopenhagen als Griegs op. 22 herausgegeben. 1892 wurden die Orchesterstücke für großes Orchester überarbeitet und neu bei Peters in Leipzig als Griegs op. 56 verlegt. Für die Eröffnung des neuen norwegischen Nationaltheaters im Jahre 1898 wurde das Stück mit der vom Komponisten wiederum bearbeiteten Partitur neu inszeniert, und eine weitere bedeutende Aufführung kam 1905 auf die Bühne, als Haakon VII., König des ganz unabhängig gewordenen Norwegen, den Thron bestieg. Inzwischen hatte sich die Konzertsuite in den internationalen Konzertsälen durchgesetzt, obwohl sie nie ganz die Beliebtheit der Musik zu *Peer Gynt* erreichte.

Griegs op. 56 besteht aus den folgenden drei Sätzen:

1. Vorspiel: „In der Königshalle". Ursprünglich als „Beim Wettstreit" bezeichnet, diente dieser Marsch als Einleitung für den zweiten Akt des Dramas. „Der Wettstreit" bezieht sich auf die Szene, in der die Brüder ihre persönlichen Verdienste hervorheben und vergleichen. Ein derartiges formelles Wetteifern galt bei den Wikingern als traditioneller Zeitvertreib und sollte die beim Bier sitzende Gesellschaft unterhalten. Im Verlauf dieser Szene verschärft sich jedoch die Rivalität und erweckt, besonders bei dem launischen König Sigurd, feindliche Gefühle, wodurch das persönliche Gefolge der beiden Hauptdarsteller in den Streit verwickelt wird. Griegs Musik beruht auf einer Gavotte für Geige und Klavier aus dem Jahre 1867.

2. Intermezzo: „Borghilds Traum". Mit der Bezeichnung „Introduktion und Melodram" gibt dieses Stück die Stimmung der Szene im ersten Akt wieder, in der Borghild, die Tochter Olafs von Dal, im Hause ihres Vaters aus unruhigen Träumen erwacht. Über ihre enge Freundschaft mit König Øjstejn wird getratscht, und um ihre Unschuld zu beweisen, hat sie sich dem Gottesurteil unterworfen, über glühendes Eisen zu schreiten. Bald darauf wird das Verhältnis zwischen den beiden Königen noch gespannter, da Sigurd, der ebenfalls im Bann ihrer Schönheit steht, versucht, sie aus ihrem Hause zu entführen. Die Musik folgt genau den von Bjørnson ausführlich angegebenen Bühnenanweisungen:

„Leise Musik beginnt, bevor sich der Vorhang hebt, und während er sich hebt, umschreibt sie ihren ruhelosen Schlaf mit schleppenden, gedämpften Passagen, die sich bis zum Ausdruck größter Angst steigern. Sie schreit, erwacht und fährt auf. Die Musik gibt die wirren Gedanken wieder, die sie beim Erwachen bedrängen und hört auf, wenn sie flüstert: „Ich schreite noch immer über das glühende Eisen." Die Musik folgt ihr wieder, während sie sich nach vorne begibt, stehen bleibt und sich an einen Stuhl lehnt ... [Hier folgt ein längerer Monolog in Versen] ... Die Musik verklingt in stillem Gram, bricht jäh ab, worauf sie sich erhebt."

Um die verlangte Stimmung herzustellen, hat Grieg gedämpfte Paukenwirbel, gestopfte Noten auf den Hörnern, Pizzicati mit zwei Fingern, zwei Piccoloflöten, die kurz anstelle der großen Flöten treten, Triangel- und Beckenschläge, sowie heftige dynamische Kontraste verwendet.

3. „Huldigungsmarsch" („Hyldningsmarsjen"). Dieser Marsch steht im dritten Akt und leitet die Szene ein, in der sich die Könige aussöhnen. Eine Bühnenanweisung besagt, dass die Musik während der Versöhnung der Brüder, die Hand in Hand abgehen, mit einer feierlichen Einleitung beginnen soll, um dann zum eigentlichen „Huldigungsmarsch" überzugehen. Damit ist dann die Bühne für den Rat oder *Husthing* bereitet, bei welchem die Könige ihre endgültige Versöhnung ankündigen. Dieser Satz ist vielfach überarbeitet und erweitert worden. Unter den späteren Zusätzen sind die Fanfaren für die Blechbläser (Anfang T. 165) und das Trio (Anfang T. 76) mit den Harfenakkorden, das an das Menuett und Trio in der Klaviersonate op. 7 erinnert, die aus dem Jahre 1865 stammt. Bemerkenswert ist auch, dass das Hauptthema des „Huldigungsmarsches", das zunächst von vier Solocelli gespielt wird, dem langsamen Satz der Cellosonate op. 36 (1882/83) ähnlich ist.

John Horton · Übersetzung: Stefan de Haan

Holberg Suite
Aus Holbergs Zeit

An Frau Erika Lie-Nissen

Edvard Grieg
(1843–1907)
Op. 40

I. Praeludium
Allegro vivace ♩ = 76

Edited by Richard Clarke
© 2013 Ernst Eulenburg Ltd, London
and Ernst Eulenburg & Co GmbH, Mainz

2

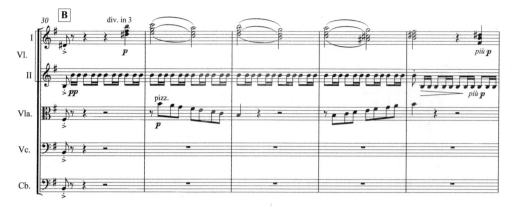

*) Lift bow / Absetzen
**) Change of bow / Bogenwechsel

II. Sarabande

Andante ♩ = 42

Un poco mosso

ritenuto poco a poco al **Tempo I** G

III. Gavotte

Allegretto ♩ = 76

10

Musette

Poco più mosso

Gavotte da Capo al Fine

IV. Air

poco rit. Q **a tempo**

V. Rigaudon

Allegro con brio ♩ = 144

18

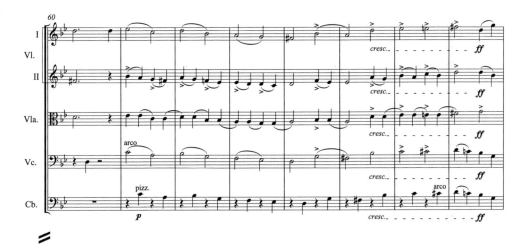

Rigaudon da Capo al Fine,
ma senza Ripetizione

Printed in China

Sigurd Jorsalfar

Edvard Grieg
(1843–1907)
Op. 56

I. Prelude
(In the King's Hall)

EAS 183

Edited by John Horton
© 2013 Ernst Eulenburg Ltd, London
and Ernst Eulenburg & Co GmbH, Mainz

22

II. Intermezzo
(Borghild's Dream)

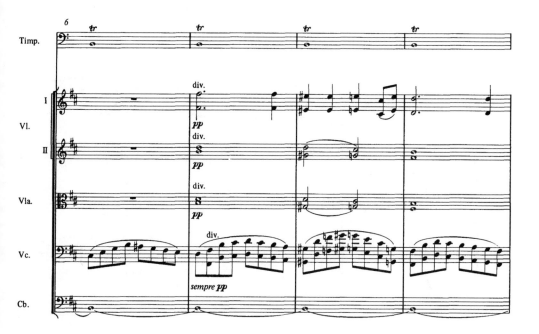

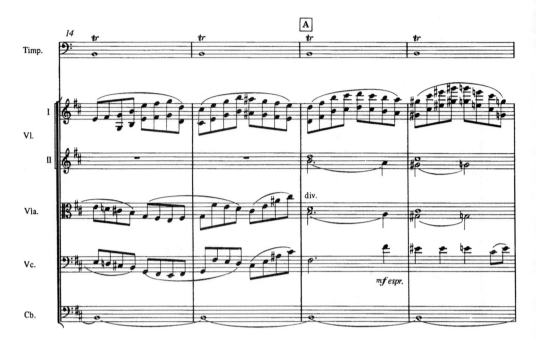

1) + = stopped notes/gestopfter Ton
2) The pizzicato double notes should not be arpeggiated but plucked with two fingers/Das zweistimmige Pizzicato nicht arpeggiert, sondern mit zwei Fingern gezupft

38

III. Homage March

EAS 183

*) The small notes in brackets for Clarinetti and Fagotti are for use only when 4 Celli are not available/
Die eingeklammerten kleinen Noten für Clarinetti und Fagotti sind nur zu benutzen, wo 4 Violoncelli nicht vorhanden

52

58

64

Printed in China